Usborne English Readers

Level 2

Arthur and the Sword in the Stone

Retold by Mairi Mackinnon

Illustrated by Teresa Martínez

English language consultant: Peter Viney

Contents

You can listen to the story online here:
www.usborneenglishreaders.com/
swordinthestone

It was the worst storm of the winter. All
night, Sir Hector and his family could
hear the wind and rain outside the castle
walls. Sir Hector's young son, Kay, was
frightened, but he knew he was safe inside
the castle.

Early in the morning, the rain stopped
and Kay looked out. The sky was bright, the
fields and rivers were full of water, and all
the roads were mud.

"There's someone coming!" shouted the
guards at the castle gate.

"I see him!" said Kay. "Who is it, Father?"

Sir Hector looked down and saw a man on a horse. The man was wearing a long dark cloak, and Sir Hector couldn't see his face. "He's alone," he told the guards. "Let him come in."

When the man came into the castle hall, Sir Hector recognized him at once. "Merlin! It's good to see you. Do you have news of my friend, the King?"

"Yes and no," said the old wizard. "You know that King Uther is old, and I am sorry to say he is not well. These are difficult times for the people of Britain."

"But my friend, I have something for you." Merlin took a bundle from under his cloak, and gave it to Sir Hector.

The bundle woke up, and started crying. "A baby?" Sir Hector gasped with surprise. "Why… who are the parents?"

"I will tell you," said Merlin, "but you must tell no one else. His name is Arthur. Keep him safe, Hector. Treat him as your own son."

Nobody noticed Kay until then. He was standing quietly behind the wizard. The little boy looked at Merlin, then looked at his father. "He's *not* my brother," he said.

A few months later, the old king died. The most important lords in the country met to choose a new king, but they couldn't agree with each other. They argued and fought, first for one lord and then for another.

Sir Hector's castle was far away from the fighting, and Kay and Arthur didn't know anything about it. They grew up quietly in the country, and learned to ride horses and fight with swords.

"Why are you learning to ride?" Kay used to say. "You'll never be a knight."

"Why not? I can use a sword just as well as you," Arthur answered.

"You can't be a knight," said Kay. "Where do you come from? Who are your family? Nobody knows. You're only here because my father is kind to you and treats you well. You're nothing, really."

"I know I can be a knight. One day, I will be," thought Arthur, but he didn't say anything.

W hen Kay was sixteen years old, he became a knight, just as he expected.

"Father, will I be a knight too next year?"
Arthur asked Sir Hector, but the old man
said nothing and looked away.

A few days later, a messenger arrived at the castle. It was the first news from the city for many months, and everyone was excited.

"There's going to be a tournament," Sir Hector told them. "All the knights in Britain will be there. Kay, you and I must go. It will be your first test as a knight."

"Please, let me come too," said Arthur.

"He's not a knight," said Kay. "He should stay here at the castle."

"I can be your squire, and serve you," said Arthur. "I can help you to get ready for the fight, and hold your horses for you."

"That *would* be very helpful," Sir Hector agreed. "All right, Arthur, you can come with us."

Kay wasn't happy, but he couldn't argue with his father. Still, he made sure that Arthur worked hard. Arthur always had to carry the heaviest bags, and find inns every evening on their way.

They reached the city. It was Arthur's first visit to a town, and he was very excited. "Stop it," said Kay. "Stop looking around and smiling. Everyone will think we are stupid country people."

There were hundreds of visitors for the tournament, and the streets were full of people and horses. "We'll never find anywhere to stay," moaned Kay. Arthur tried one inn after another, and at last he found one, a little way from the tournament field.

The next morning, he helped Sir Hector and Kay to get ready. "You look really good," he told Kay. "I'm sure you'll do well." Then he brought the horses and they rode to the tournament together.

On the road, Kay stopped suddenly.
"My sword! Where's my sword?"

"I thought you had it," said Arthur.
"Stupid boy! I suppose you left it at the
inn. Go back and fetch it. Hurry, now!"

It took Arthur a long time to reach the inn. He had to ride slowly, through crowds of people who were all going the other way. When he arrived, the streets and houses were empty. Everyone was at the tournament already, or on their way there.

The door of the inn was locked, and nobody came to open it.

"Kay will kill me," thought Arthur.

He looked around. Near the inn was a large square, with houses all around it. Arthur didn't remember seeing it the night before.

In the middle of the square was a rock, with some writing on it. Arthur didn't stop to read the writing, but he noticed that there was something fixed in the rock.

"A sword!" he gasped.

"Why did you take so long?" asked Kay. "Here, give me that." He looked at the sword. "Wait, this isn't my sword. I don't recognize it."

"It's a good one, though, isn't it?" said Arthur.

"Where did you get it?" asked Kay, and Arthur started to explain. Kay didn't wait for him to finish, but went to find Sir Hector.

"Father!" he shouted. "Look what I
have – it's the sword from the stone! You
remember, the one we saw in the square.
That means I will be the next king of
Britain, doesn't it?"

Sir Hector looked at him. "Really?
Did you pull it out of the stone, Kay?"

"No," said Arthur quietly. "I did."

Kay looked around angrily. "You couldn't do that! You're not even a knight!"

"Let's go back to the stone," said Sir Hector, "and then you can show me what happened."

They reached the empty square, and this time, Arthur read the writing on the rock:

Whoever pulls the sword from this stone shall be the King of Britain.

"A *king*?" he wondered. "Is that possible?"

"Put the sword back, Arthur," said Sir Hector, and Arthur did. The sword went into the rock, as easily as a knife going into water.

"Now, Kay, try pulling it out."

Kay tried, but the sword was fixed again and he couldn't move it at all.

Sir Hector tried, too, but nothing happened. "That's what I expected," he said. Then Arthur took the sword, and this time it came out easily.

Sir Hector knelt down. "Arthur, you are the true king, and I will serve you for the rest of my life."

"There is something I must tell you. I am not your real father, Arthur. The wizard Merlin brought you to me when you were a baby. Your father was the last king, Uther Pendragon. The king was dying, and because you were so young, your life was in terrible danger."

"Merlin thought that the old lords might kill you. He brought you from the castle where you were born, and told me to keep you safe."

"I couldn't tell you all this before, but now I can see you are ready.

Put the sword back one last time. Everyone must see this."

Sir Hector and Kay rode back to the tournament to tell everyone the news. The lords and knights followed them to the square. They were amazed to see Arthur. "That can't be the king," they said. "He's only a boy!"

But in front of the whole crowd, Arthur pulled the sword from the stone again and held it high.

Everyone was quiet, and then they began to cheer. "Long live the King!" they shouted. "Long live King Arthur!"

About King Arthur

People have told stories about King Arthur for hundreds of years. One of the first people to write about him was Geoffrey of Monmouth. His book about the kings of Britain was very popular. It included Arthur and Uther Pendragon, his father.

People say Arthur was king in England 1,500 years ago, although no one is sure if he was real or not. The stories say that when he grew up, he lived in a fantastic castle, called Camelot. Merlin was his friend for the rest of his life, and together they found *another* sword, the magic Excalibur.

These kinds of stories are called 'legends'. They are about things that happened in a country long ago, and although they may not be completely true, people still like to tell them.

Activities

The answers are on page 40.

The people in the story

Pick one sentence for each person.

Merlin

Arthur

Kay

Sir Hector

A.
He gave Sir Hector a baby.

B.
The wizard Merlin was his father.

C.
He let Arthur come to the tournament.

D.
He grew up in the city.

E.
He pulled the sword out of the stone.

F.
He didn't want to stay at the inn.

G.
He couldn't ride very well.

H.
He went to fight in the tournament.

Mixed-up story

Can you put these pictures and sentences in order?

A.

When Kay was sixteen years old, he became a knight.

B.

There was a sword, fixed in the rock.

C.

Arthur went with Kay to the tournament.

D.

Kay and Arthur grew up in the country.

E.

The sword came out easily.

F.

A man on a horse arrived at Sir Hector's castle.

G.

"Go back and fetch my sword," said Kay.

H.

"His name is Arthur," said Merlin.

I.

Everyone shouted "Long live King Arthur!"

Say why...

Choose the right ending for each sentence.

1.

Merlin brought Arthur to Sir Hector, because...

a) ...the baby was in danger.

b) ...the King was dead.

2.

Arthur was very excited, because...

a) ...it was his first visit to a town.

b) ...it was his first test as a knight.

3.

Arthur had to ride back to the inn, because...

a) ...he didn't want to watch the fight.

b) ...he needed to find Kay's sword.

4.

Sir Hector knelt down for Arthur, because...

a) ...Arthur was the true King.

b) ...Arthur was his son.

Sir Hector

Choose a word to finish each sentence.

1.

.... him as your own son.

Treat   Look   Keep

2.

You can .... with us to the tournament.

arrive   fight   come

3.

Did you .... it out of the stone?

pick   push   pull

4.

I will .... you for the rest of my life.

leave   follow   carry

Long live the King!

Which three things *can't* you see in the picture?

a castle   lords

Arthur   Sir Hector   Kay

Merlin   a sword

knights   a baby   a stone

a dog   horses

Word list

argue (v) to speak angrily because you don't agree.

bundle (n) something that is held together for carrying.

cheer (v) when you cheer, you shout
to show you agree and are happy.

cloak (n) a kind of long coat without sleeves.

crowd (n) a lot of people together in one place.

fixed (adj) if something is fixed, it can't move.

gasp (v) to make a noise that
shows you are surprised or hurt.

guard (n) someone who keeps
a building or a person safe.

hall (n) the largest and most important room
in a castle, or the first room in a house.

inn (n) a place where you can pay to eat
and sleep when you are on a journey.

kneel down (v) **knelt down** to put one or
both knees on the ground, often to show
that someone is more important than you.

knight (n) a man who serves the
king or a lord, and will fight for him.

locked (adj) closed with a key.

lord (n) a rich and important man.

messenger (n) someone who takes
news and messages to people.

moan (v) to make a noise or say something
to show that you are unhappy or hurt.

mud (n) when it rains, wet ground becomes mud.

reach (v) to arrive at a place.

serve (v) to help someone by doing
things for them. Often, you serve people
who are more important than you.

Sir an ordinary man is called Mr. but a
knight is called Sir. (You can also use Sir
when you are speaking politely to a man.)

square (n) an open space with buildings around it.

squire (n) someone who serves a knight,
and hopes to become a knight one day.

test (n) something that you must
do to show how good you are.

tournament (n) a competition for knights.

treat (v) the way that you are with
another person. If you treat someone
well, you are good and kind to them.

visitor (n) someone who comes
to visit a person or a place.

Answers

The people in the story
Merlin – A
Arthur – E
Kay – H
Sir Hector – C

Mixed-up story
F, H, D, A, C,
G, B, E, I

Say why...
1. A
2. A
3. B
4. A

Sir Hector
1. Treat
2. come
3. pull
4. follow

Long live the King!
These things aren't in the picture:
Merlin, a castle, a baby

You can find information about other
Usborne English Readers here:
www.usborneenglishreaders.com

Designed by Hope Reynolds
Series designer: Laura Nelson
Edited by Jane Chisholm
With thanks to Rosie Hore
Digital imaging: John Russell

Page 32: Geoffrey of Monmouth © Hulton Fine Art Collection via Getty Images

First published in 2017 by Usborne Publishing Ltd.,
Usborne House, 83-85 Saffron Hill, London EC1N 8RT, England.
www.usborne.com Copyright © 2017 Usborne Publishing Ltd.